ISBN-10: 0-692-21232-9
ISBN-13: 978-0-692-21232-5

The WilderWay LLC
www.TheWilderWay.com

Printed in China

CHARLOTTE, WANDER ON.

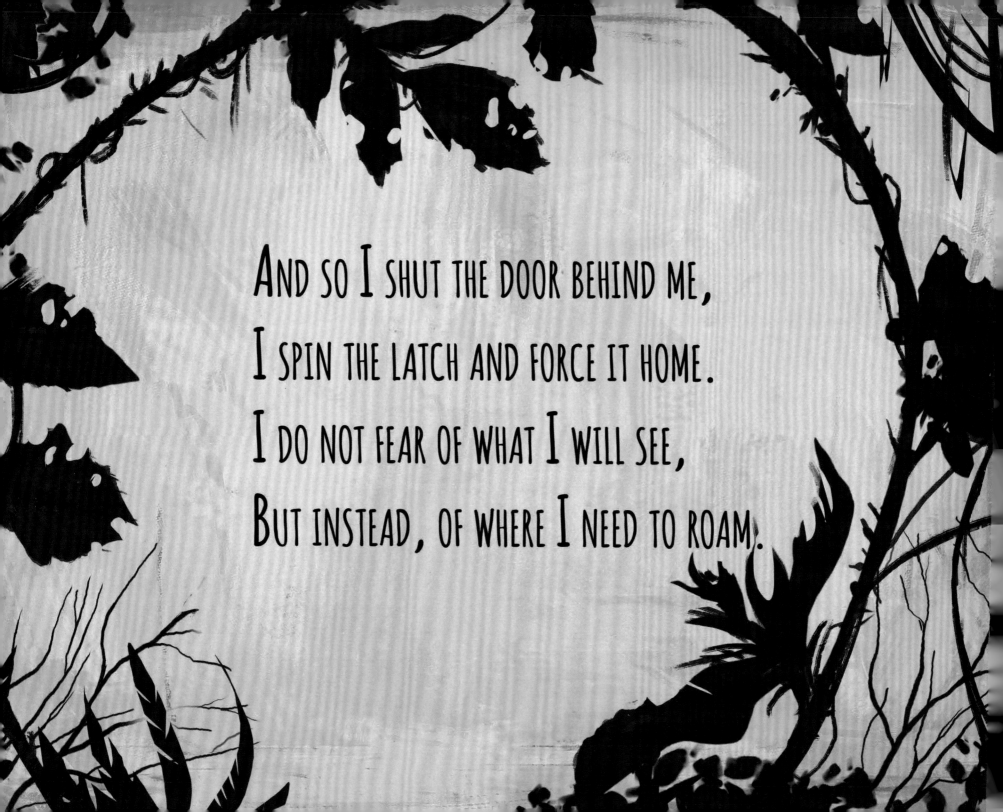

And so I shut the door behind me,
I spin the latch and force it home.
I do not fear of what I will see,
But instead, of where I need to roam.

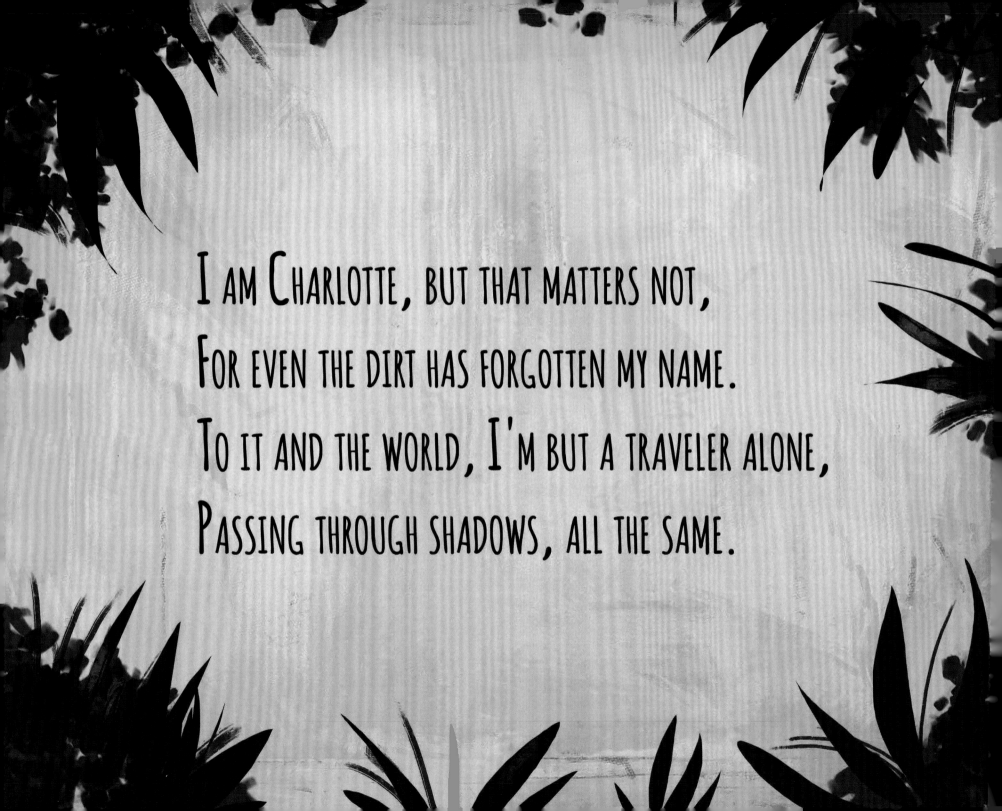

I am Charlotte, but that matters not,
For even the dirt has forgotten my name.
To it and the world, I'm but a traveler alone,
Passing through shadows, all the same.

To my sweet Charlotte!

May you find what we all seek!

There are no stars to guide my steps,
Nor moon to pry back the dark.
I haven't a lamp to light my way,
Nor crumbs to leave my mark.

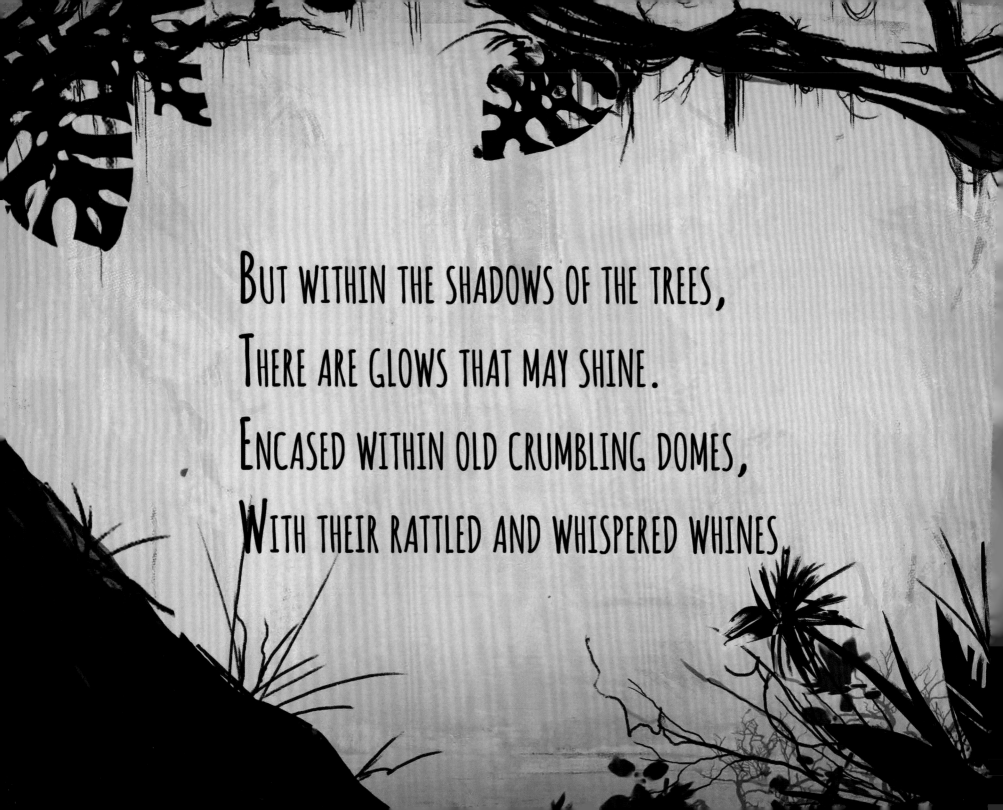

But within the shadows of the trees,
There are glows that may shine.
Encased within old crumbling domes,
With their rattled and whispered whines

Bones wrapped in mossy skin,
Yet bodies strong as stone.
Chests heave with each struggled breath,
And let loose another moan.

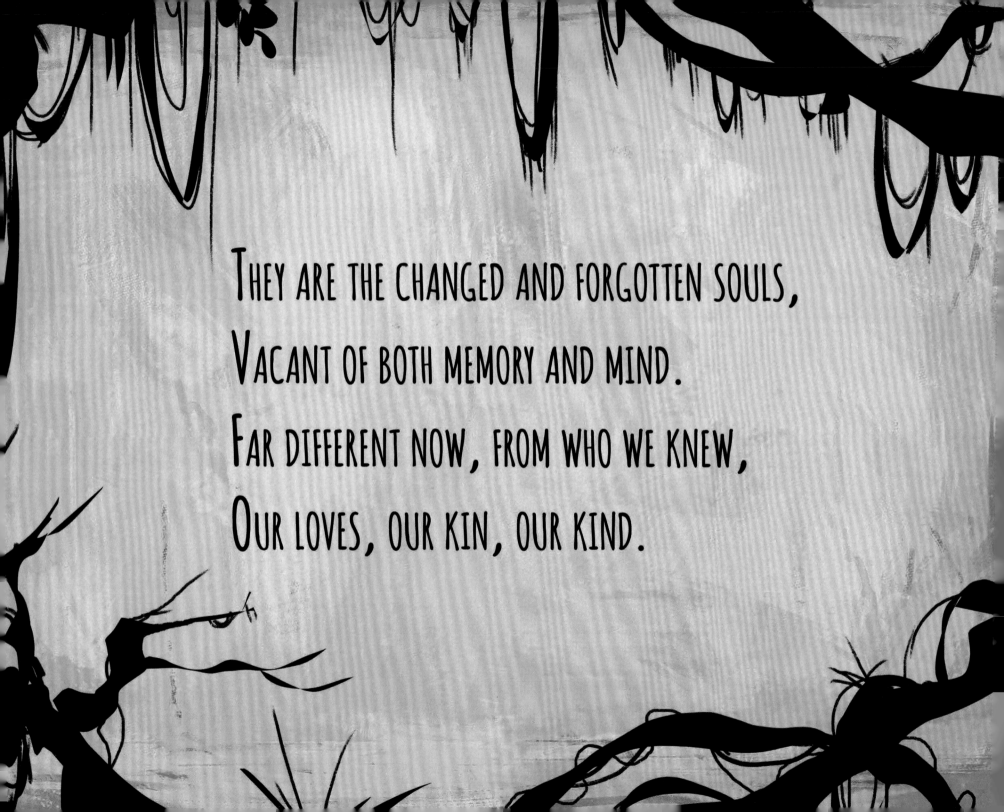

They are the changed and forgotten souls,
Vacant of both memory and mind.
Far different now, from who we knew,
Our loves, our kin, our kind.

I've often thought to steal a glance,
And discover a friendly face.
To take them from these horrors,
And return them to their place.

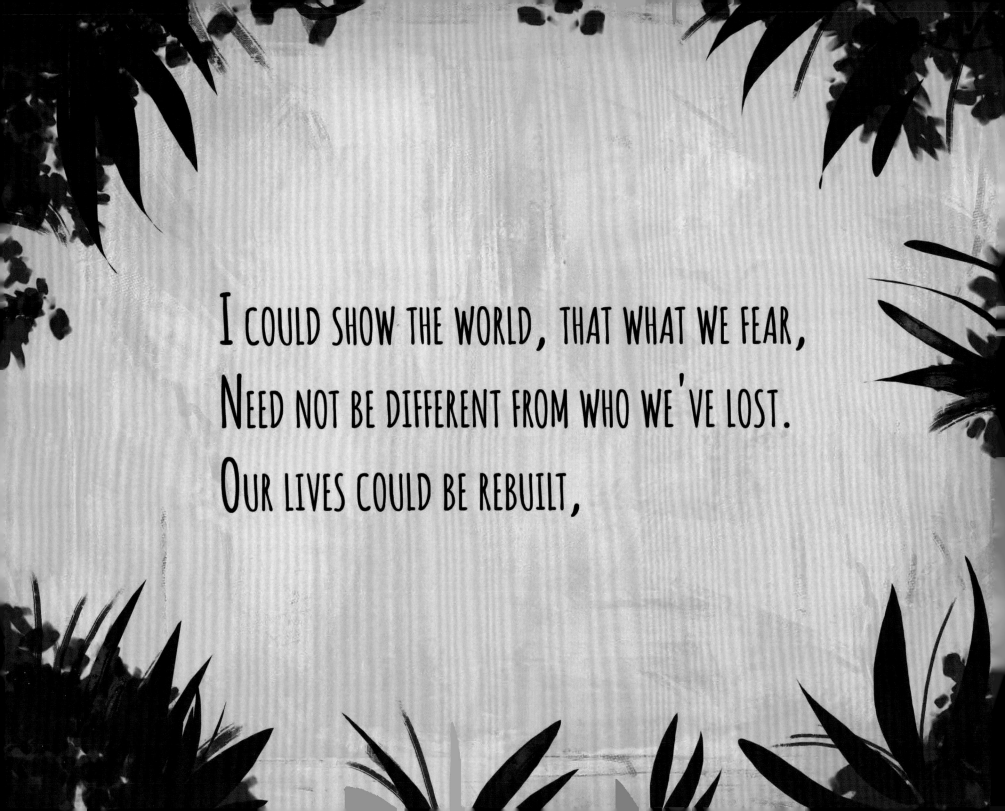

I could show the world, that what we fear,
Need not be different from who we've lost.
Our lives could be rebuilt,

Yet they say our safety, the cost.

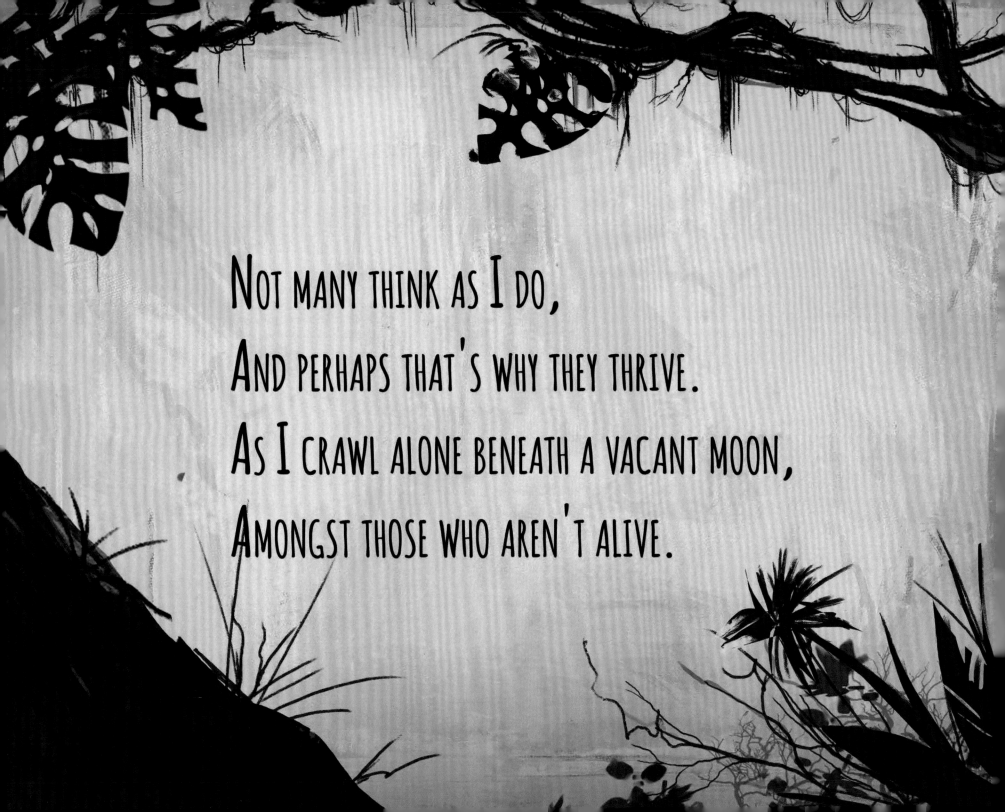

Not many think as I do,

And perhaps that's why they thrive.

As I crawl alone beneath a vacant moon,

Amongst those who aren't alive.

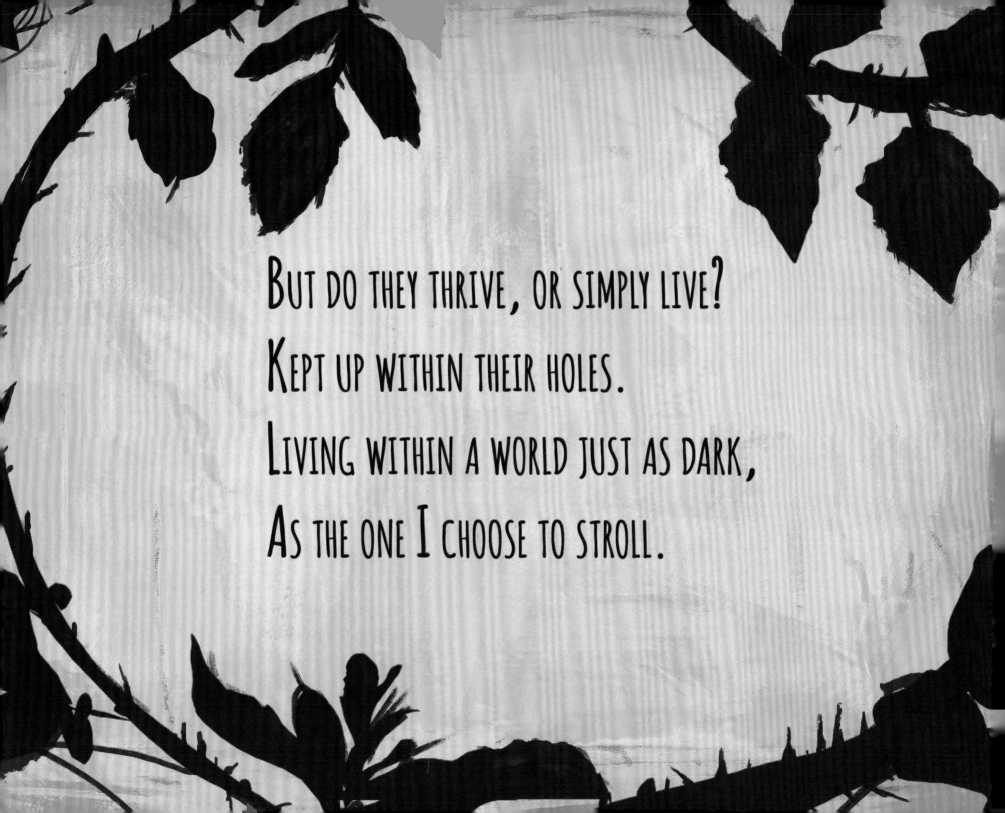

But do they thrive, or simply live?
Kept up within their holes.
Living within a world just as dark,
As the one I choose to stroll.

But their lives are not of my concern,
For I do not plan on going back.
I seek a far more important prize,
Than the safety they offer, and the hope they lack.

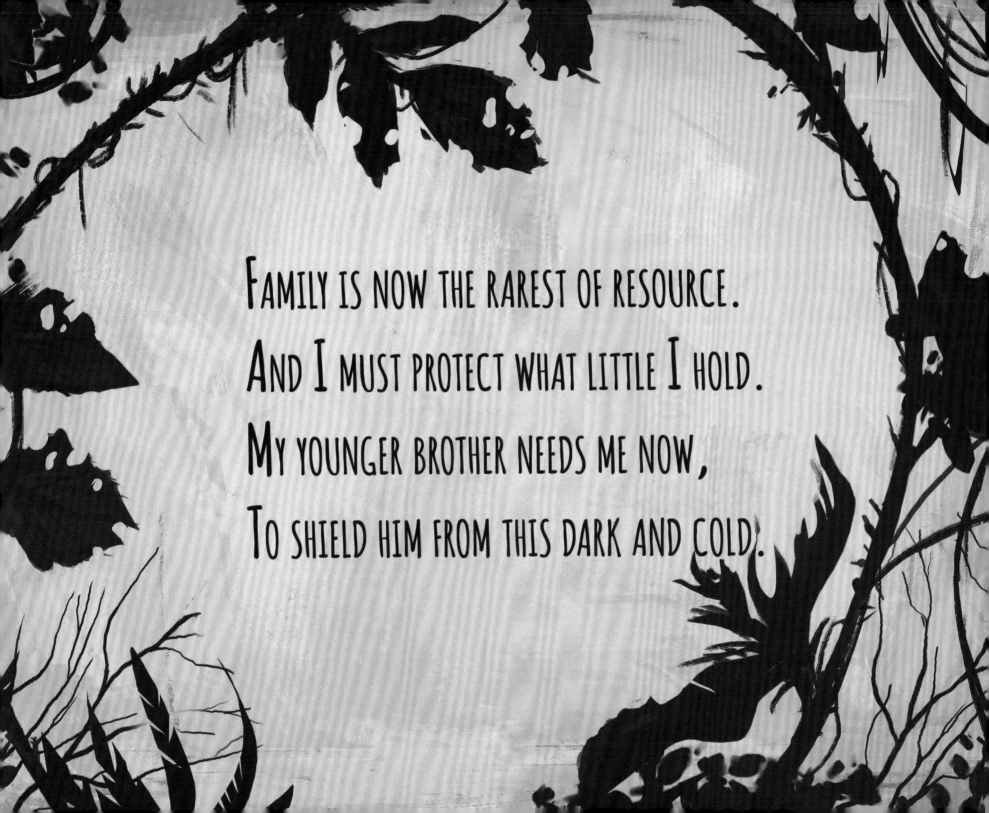

Family is now the rarest of resource.
And I must protect what little I hold.
My younger brother needs me now,
To shield him from this dark and cold.

I cannot return to help him yet,
And it pains me to stay far out here.
I haven't the means to save him from this,
But with each step to the end, I draw near.

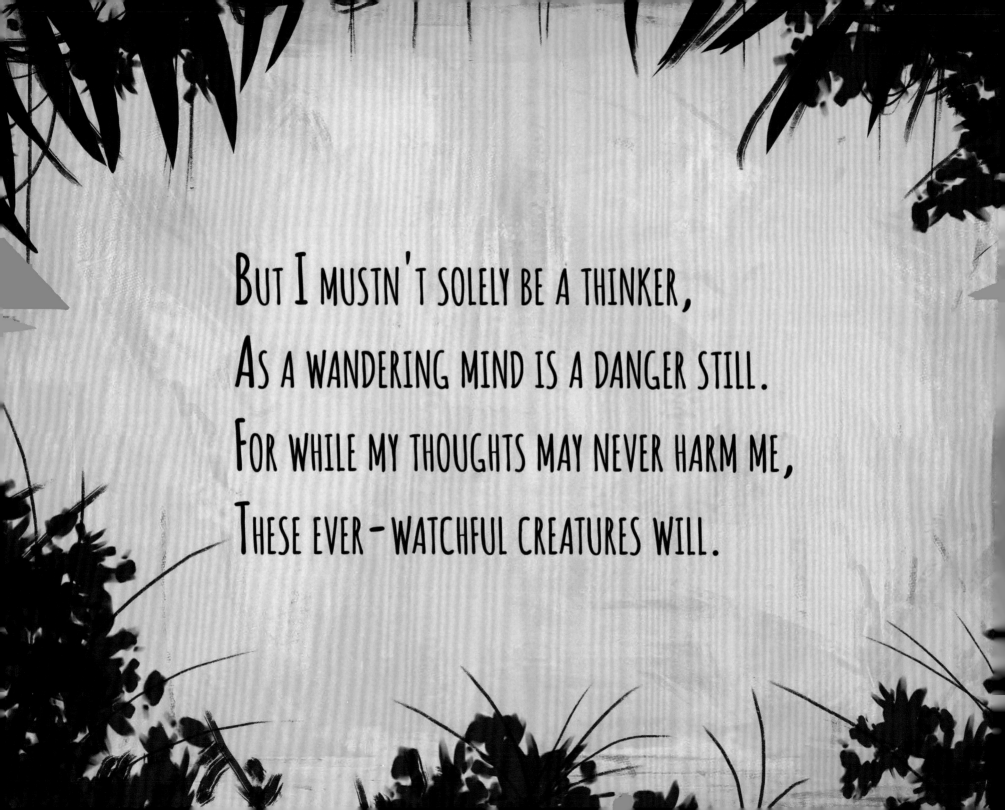

But I mustn't solely be a thinker,
As a wandering mind is a danger still.
For while my thoughts may never harm me,
These ever-watchful creatures will.

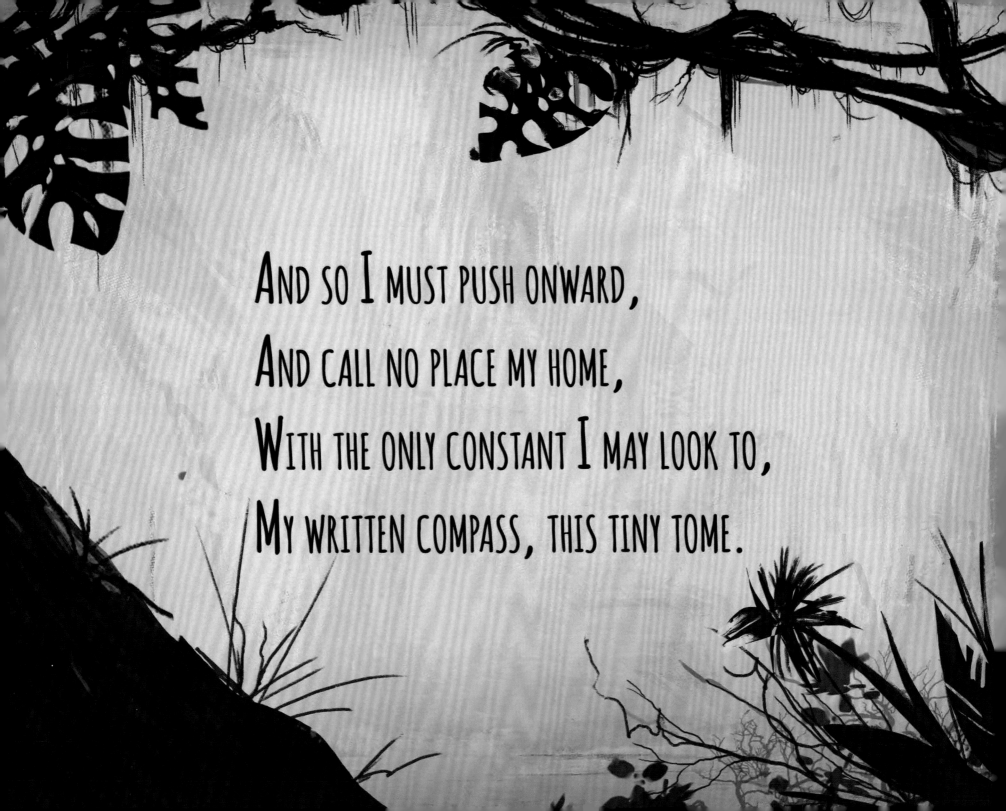

And so I must push onward,
And call no place my home,
With the only constant I may look to,
My written compass, this tiny tome.

It is what guides me now,
Written by a writer passed.
My grandmother, a true eccentric,
But who knew what dreams to chase and cast.

She told me stories and wove me tales,
Of an answer hidden away,
Deep beneath what we could see,
To be found and used some day.

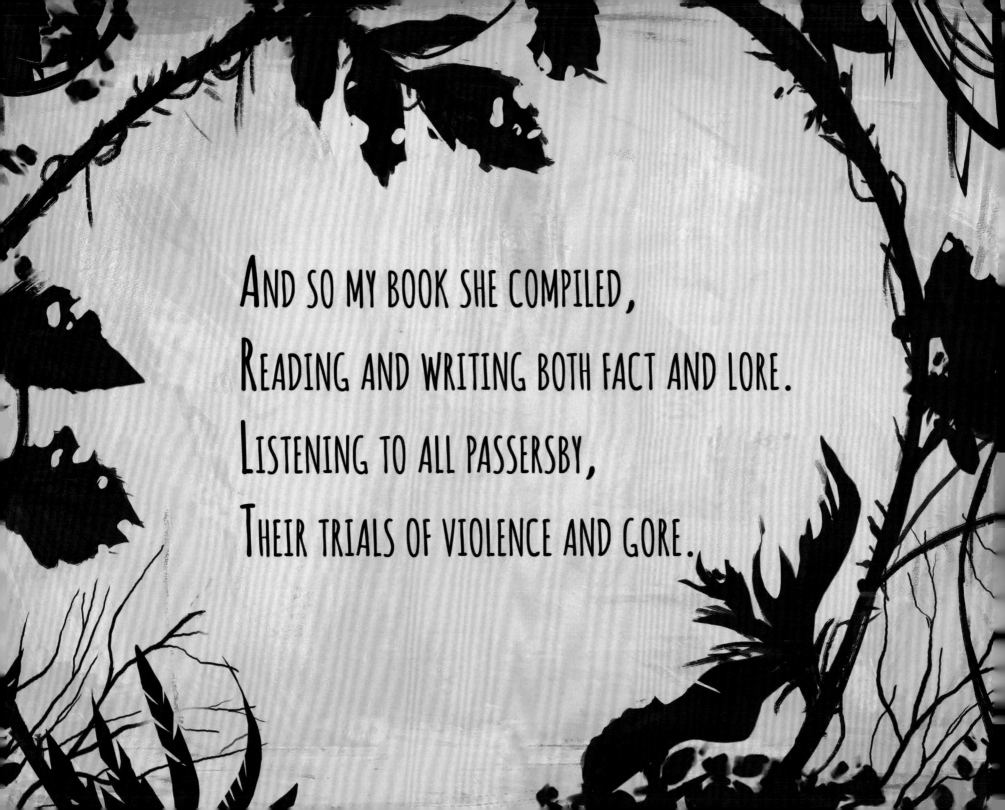

And so my book she compiled,
Reading and writing both fact and lore.
Listening to all passersby,
Their trials of violence and gore.

But at the end of every story,
And from each of the travelers' tales,
The same prize described,
Yet hunted to no avail.

I told her I would take the book,
And use it as my guide.
To seek its ends, and search the world,
I'd never run, nor ever hide.

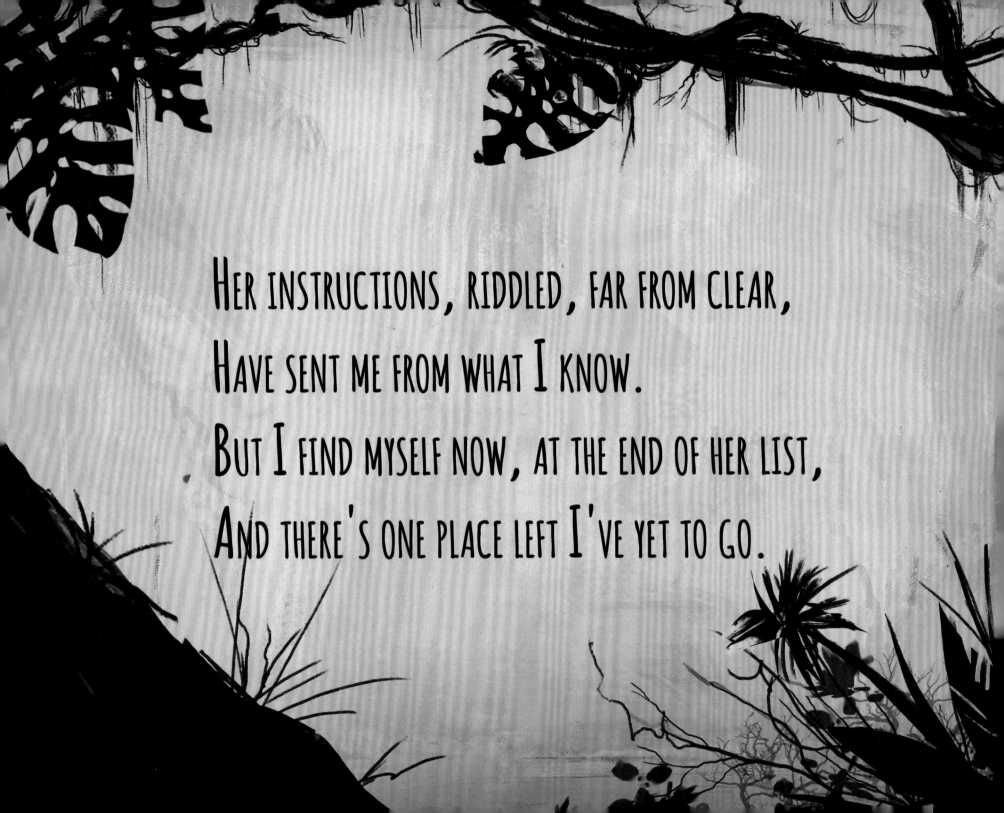

Her instructions, riddled, far from clear,
Have sent me from what I know.
But I find myself now, at the end of her list,
And there's one place left I've yet to go.

I pause. I stare. My neck craned far,
At what lays its shadow over me.
A gnarled and mangled and tortured mass.
The roots of a great grey tree.

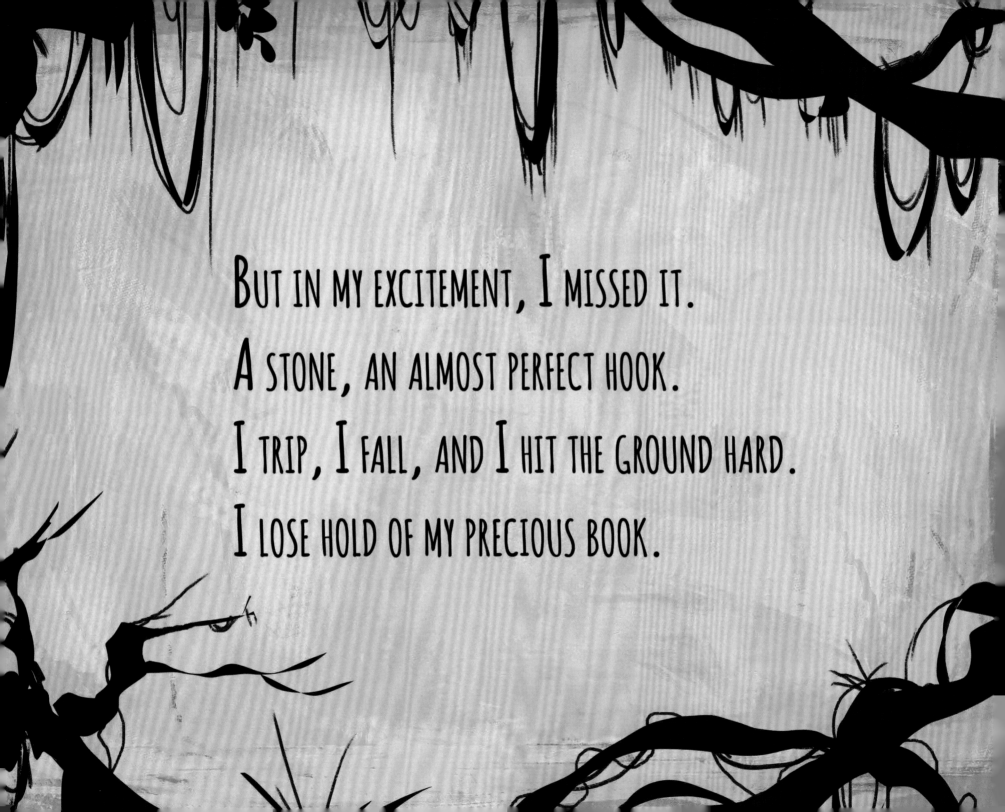

But in my excitement, I missed it.
A stone, an almost perfect hook.
I trip, I fall, and I hit the ground hard.
I lose hold of my precious book.

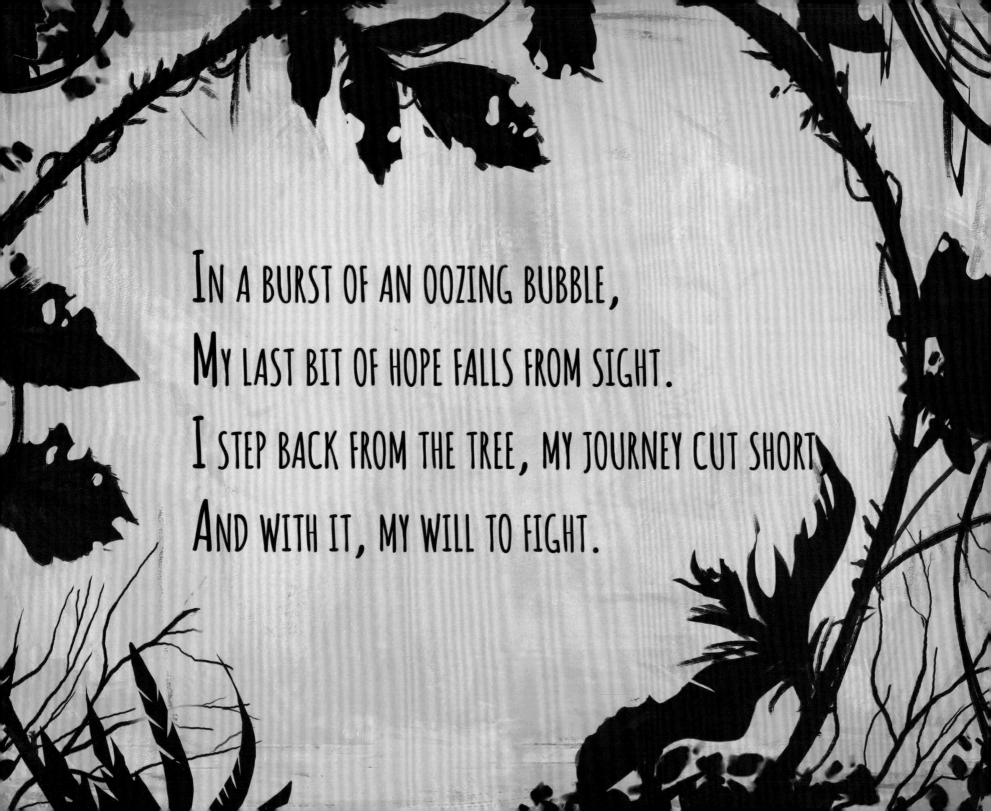

In a burst of an oozing bubble,
My last bit of hope falls from sight.
I step back from the tree, my journey cut short
And with it, my will to fight.

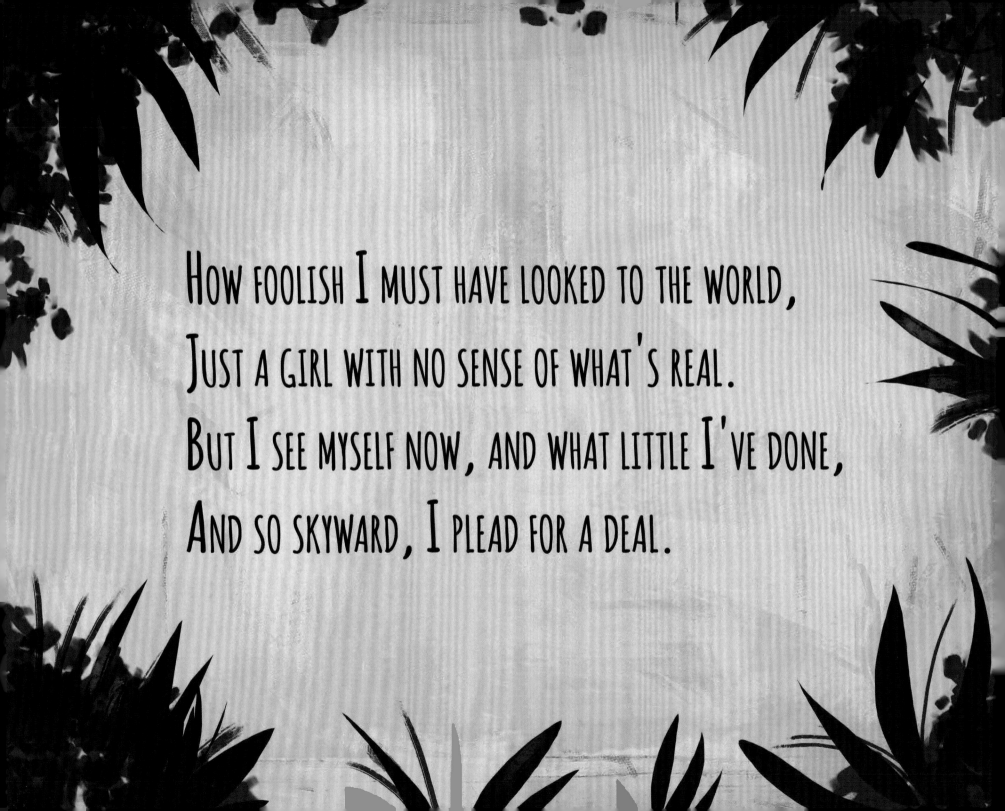

How foolish I must have looked to the world,

Just a girl with no sense of what's real.

But I see myself now, and what little I've done,

And so skyward, I plead for a deal.

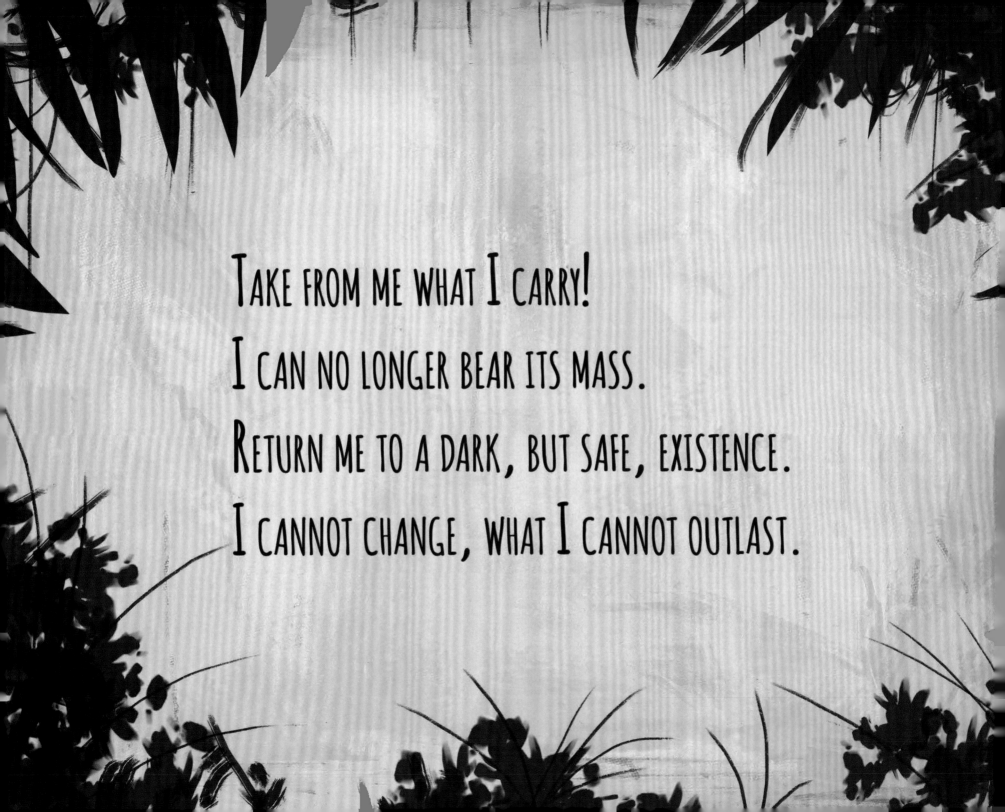

Take from me what I carry!
I can no longer bear its mass.
Return me to a dark, but safe, existence.
I cannot change, what I cannot outlast.

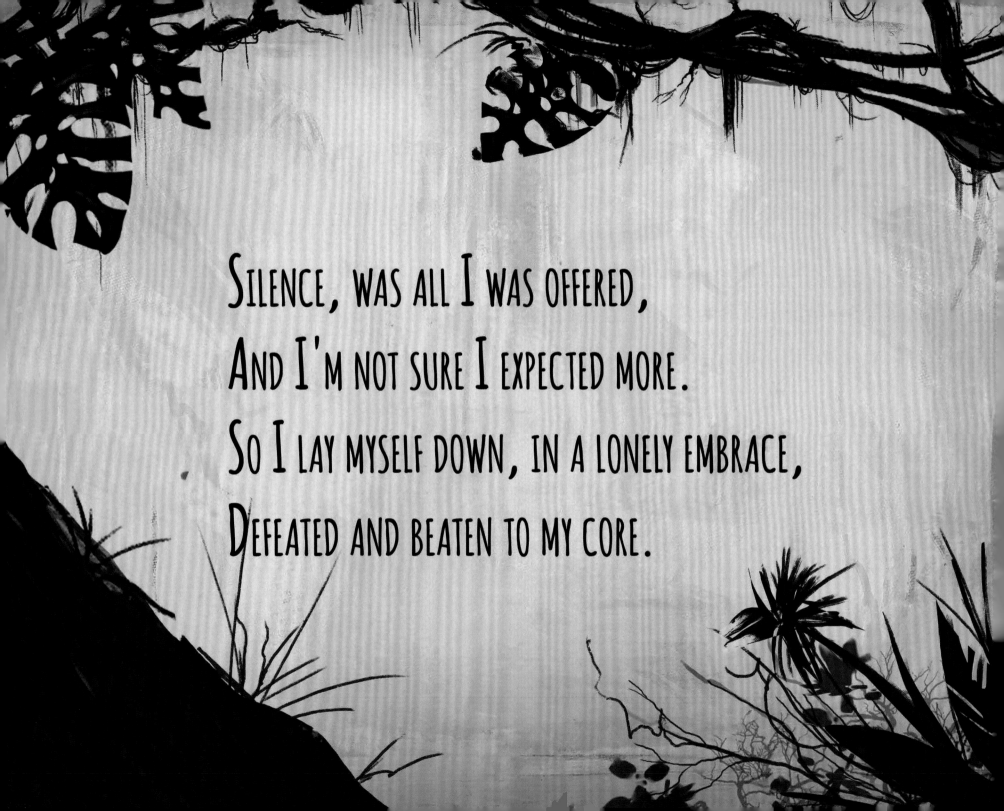

Silence, was all I was offered,
And I'm not sure I expected more.
So I lay myself down, in a lonely embrace,
Defeated and beaten to my core.

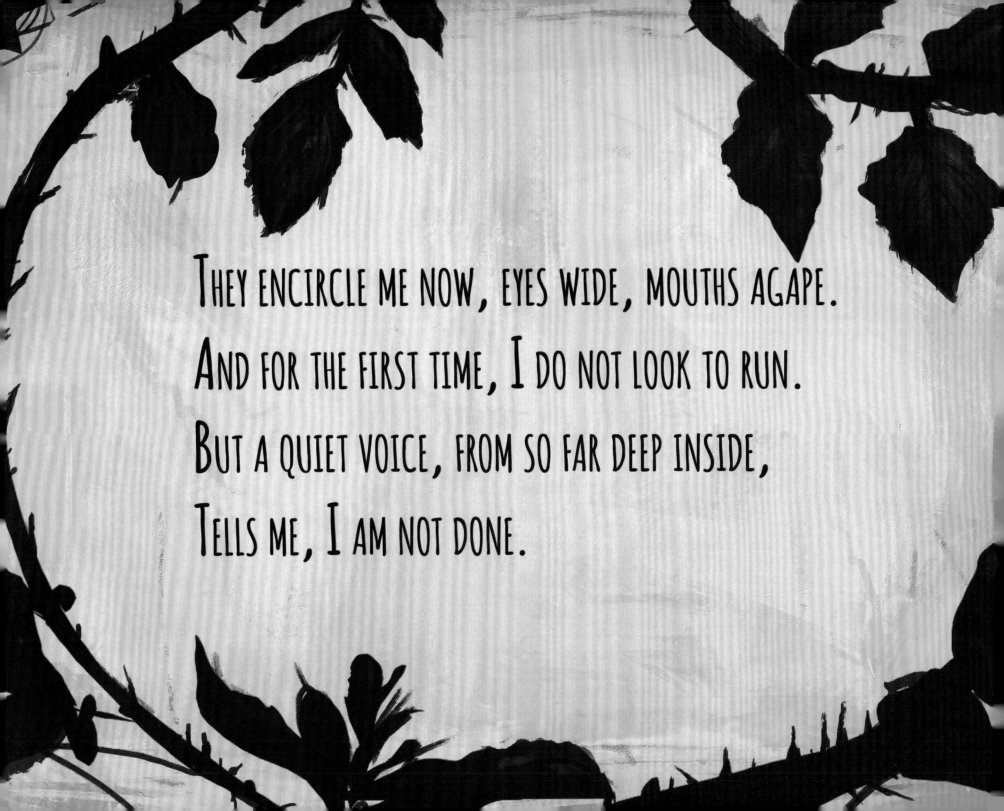

They encircle me now, eyes wide, mouths agape.

And for the first time, I do not look to run.

But a quiet voice, from so far deep inside,

Tells me, I am not done.

This darkness muffles almost every sound,
But I can hear my grandmother through it all.
She jokes and mocks me, like she would,
And like I would, I meet her call.

Oh, my sweet Charlotte, this is quite all right.
You just lie there and take a rest.
I'm sure you've done all that you can.
I'm sure you've tried your best.

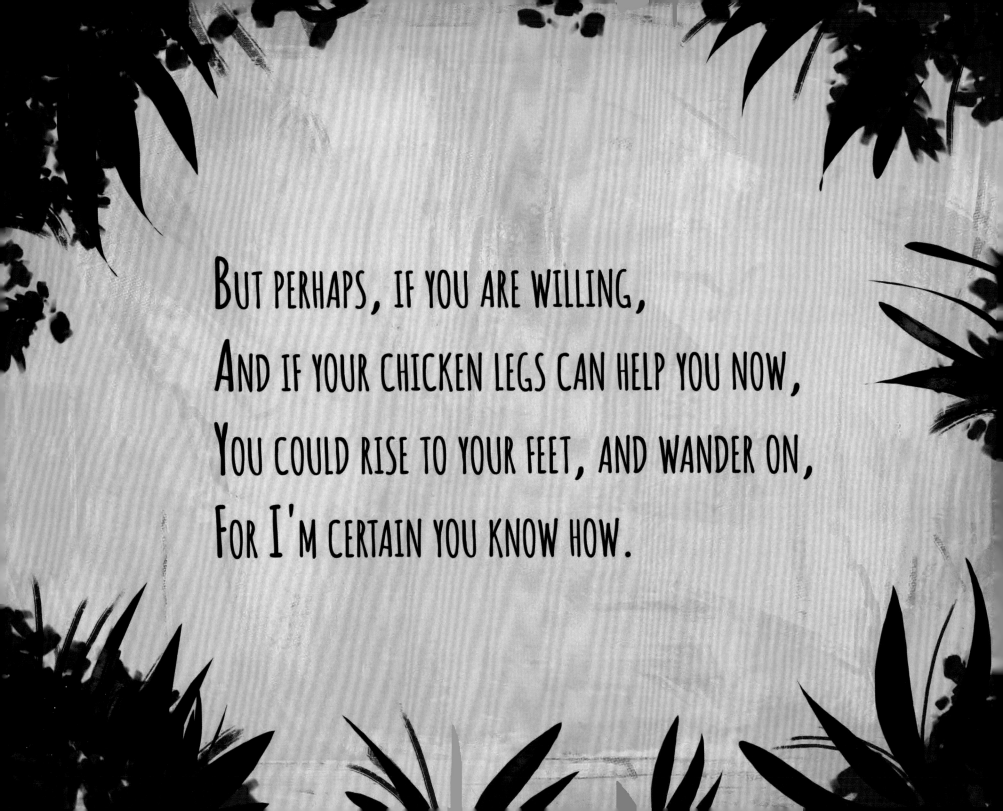

But perhaps, if you are willing,
And if your chicken legs can help you now,
You could rise to your feet, and wander on,
For I'm certain you know how.

Book or no book, you remember the way.

You've read it more times than I.

So brush yourself off, deny these creatures their meal,

And give this a final try!

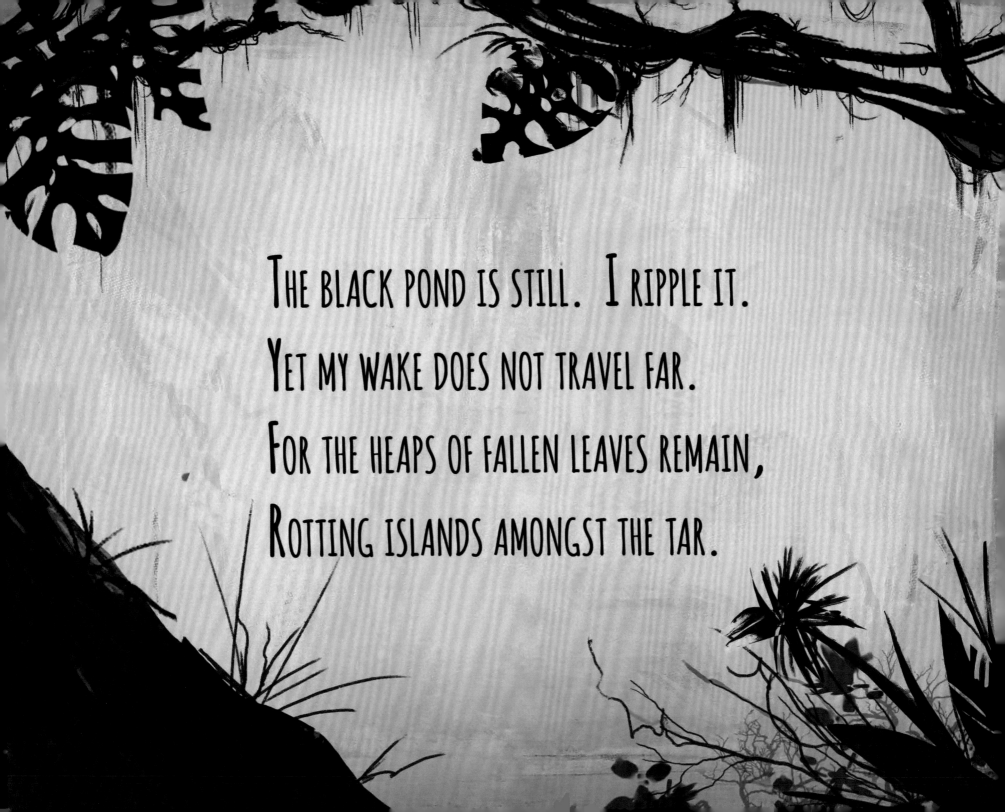

The black pond is still. I ripple it.
Yet my wake does not travel far.
For the heaps of fallen leaves remain,
Rotting islands amongst the tar.

I trudge the muck, and I near the tree.
Stale air, an aura grand.
I recite the lines I've memorized,
Miss not the book in my hand.

Dip below the dauntless diggers' den.
Deep beneath the dirt and dust.

SLIP ALONG THIS HOLLOW SERPENT'S SIDES.
SCRAPE AGAINST ITS RIBS OF RUST.

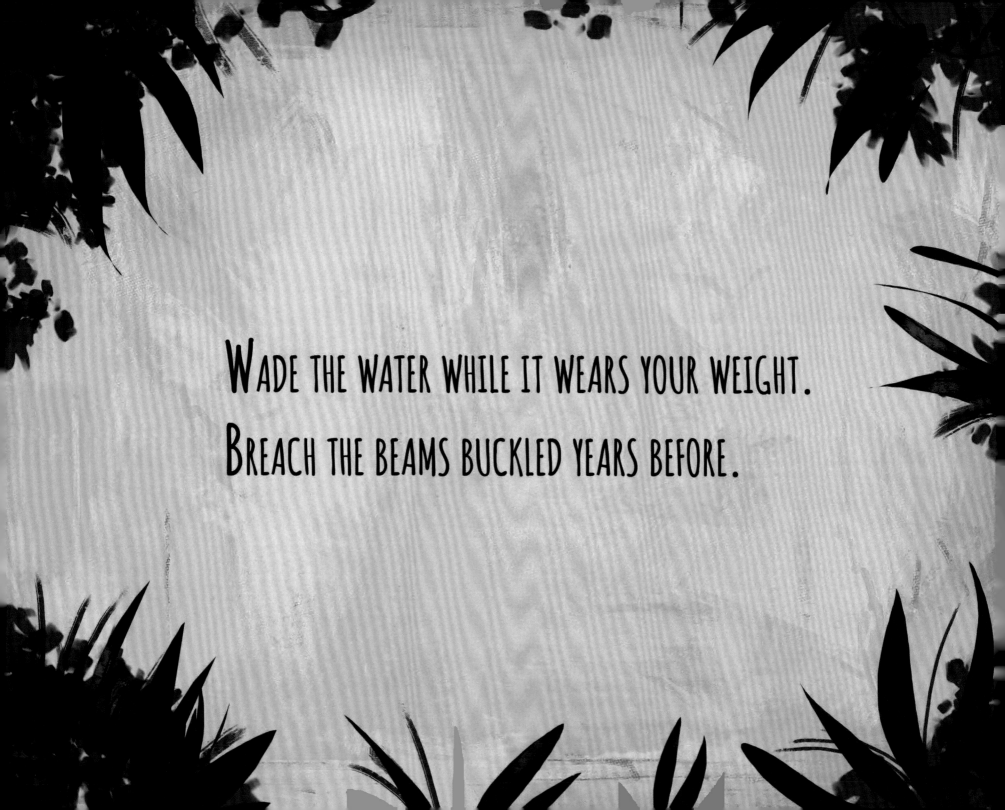

Wade the water while it wears your weight.
Breach the beams buckled years before.

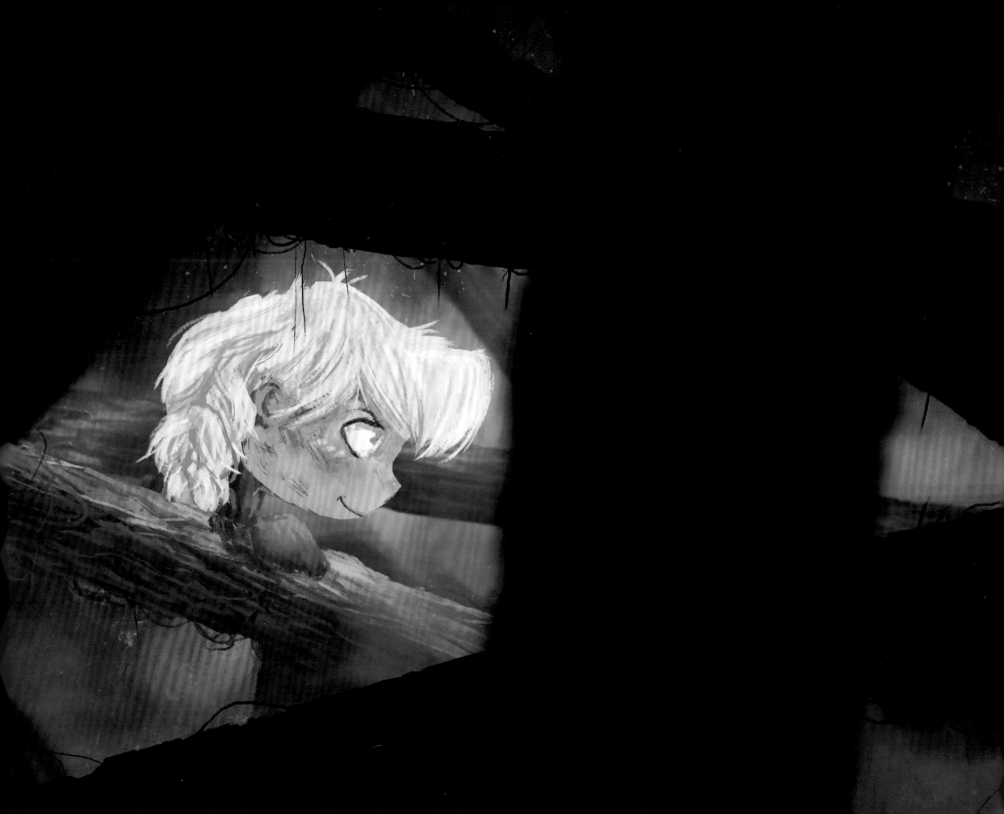

Sure the sharpened shovel from its sheath.

Force from you the fallen ore.

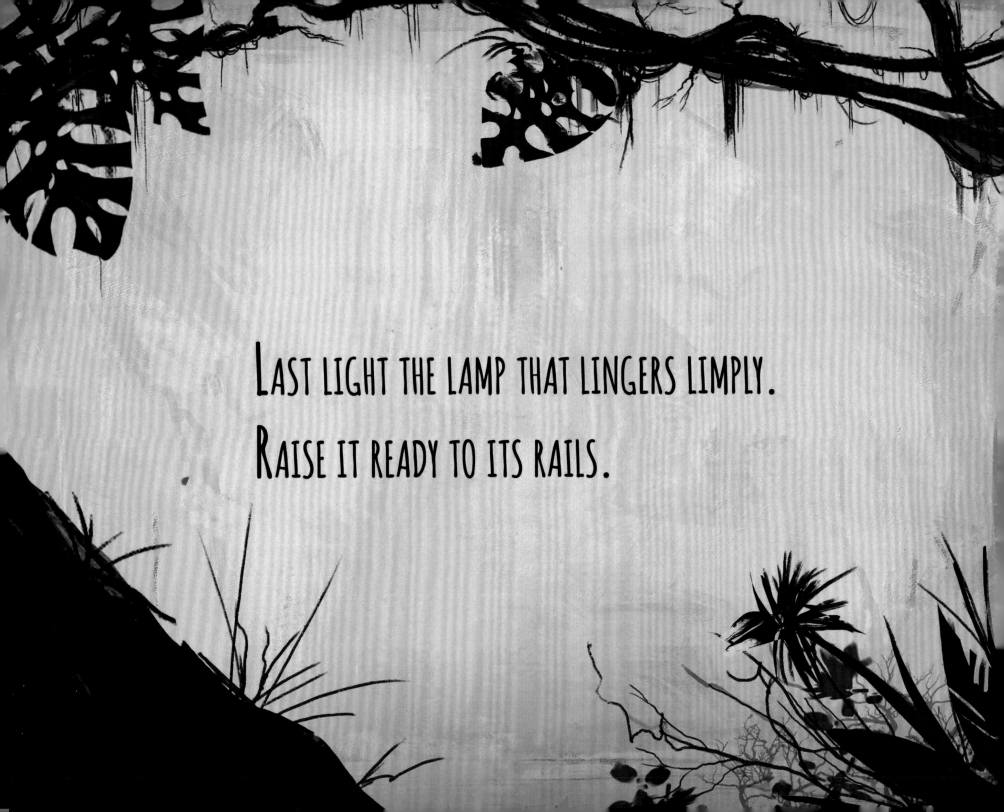

Last light the lamp that lingers limply.
Raise it ready to its rails.

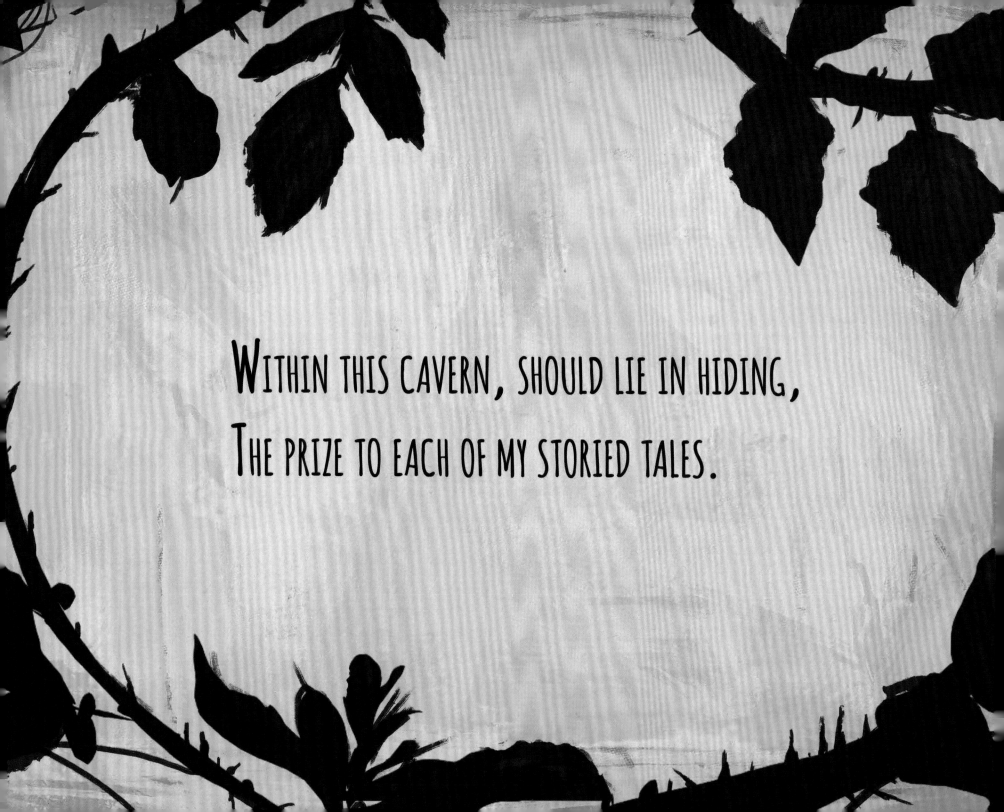

Within this cavern, should lie in hiding,
The prize to each of my storied tales.

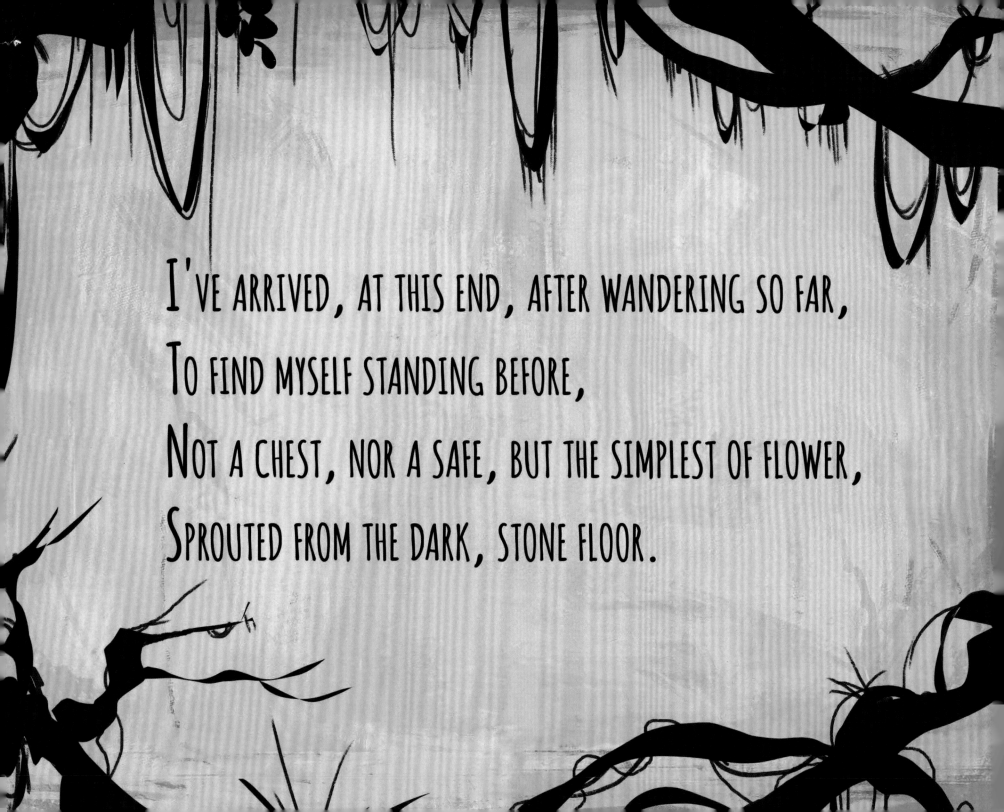

I've arrived, at this end, after wandering so far,

To find myself standing before,

Not a chest, nor a safe, but the simplest of flower,

Sprouted from the dark, stone floor.

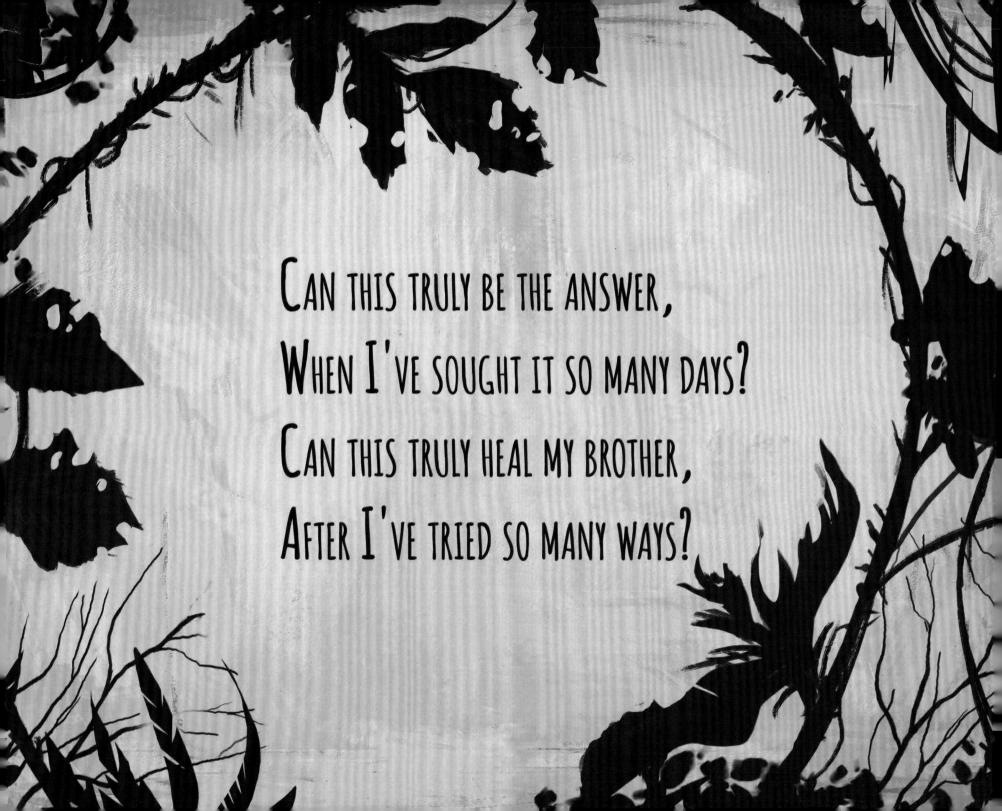

Can this truly be the answer,
When I've sought it so many days?
Can this truly heal my brother,
After I've tried so many ways?

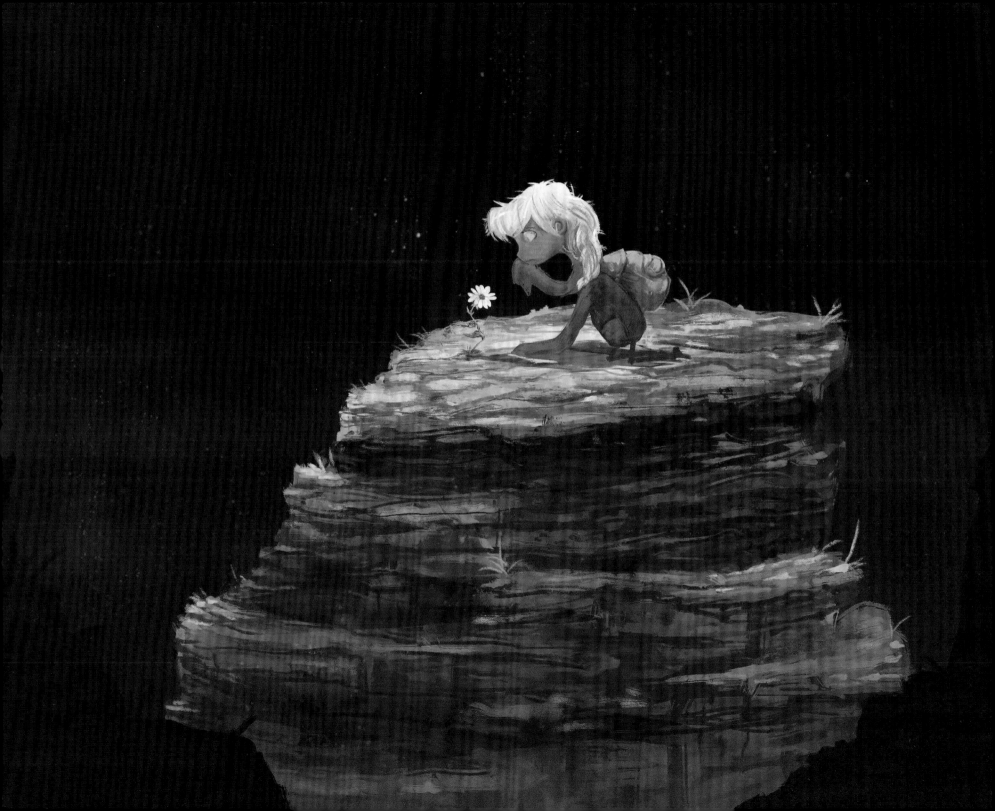

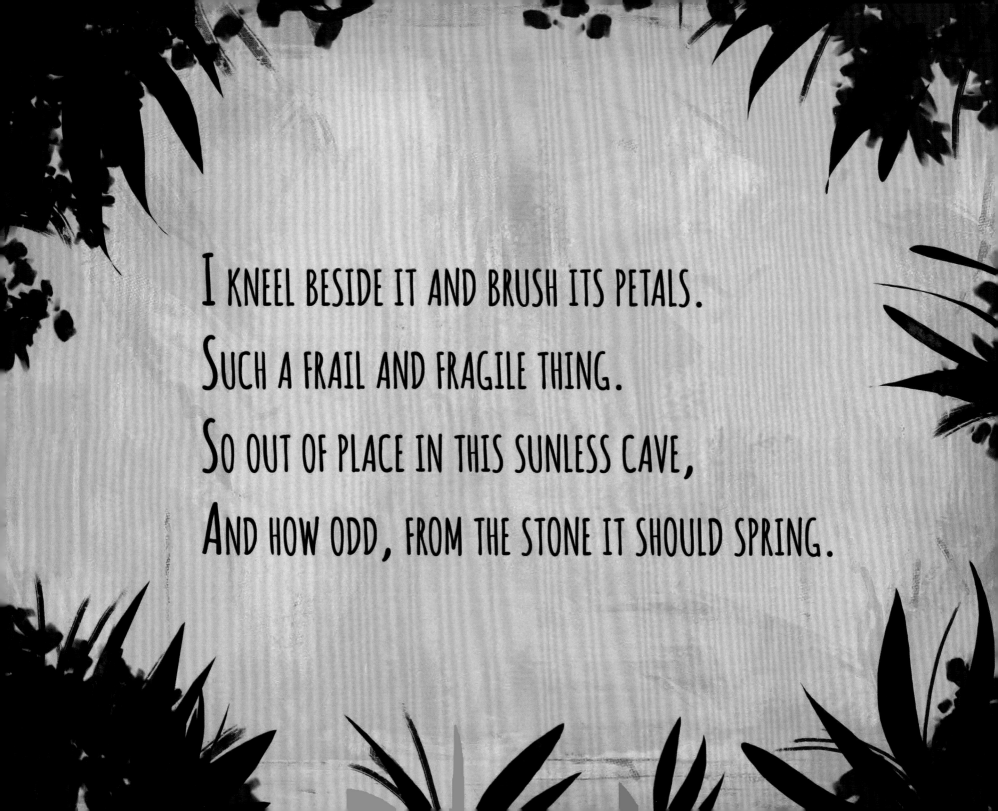

I KNEEL BESIDE IT AND BRUSH ITS PETALS.

SUCH A FRAIL AND FRAGILE THING.

SO OUT OF PLACE IN THIS SUNLESS CAVE,

AND HOW ODD, FROM THE STONE IT SHOULD SPRING.

But through my days within this darkness,

If I've learned any lesson at all,

It's the strength of the heart, and the will of the mind,

Not the vessel, be it large or so small.

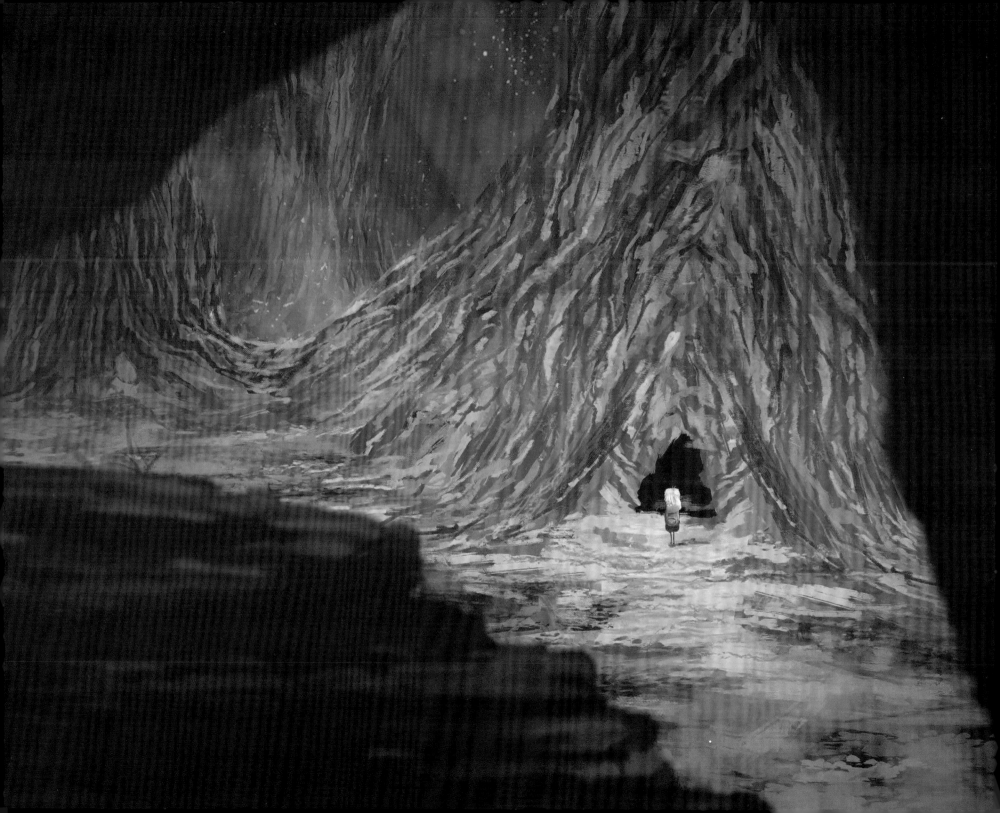

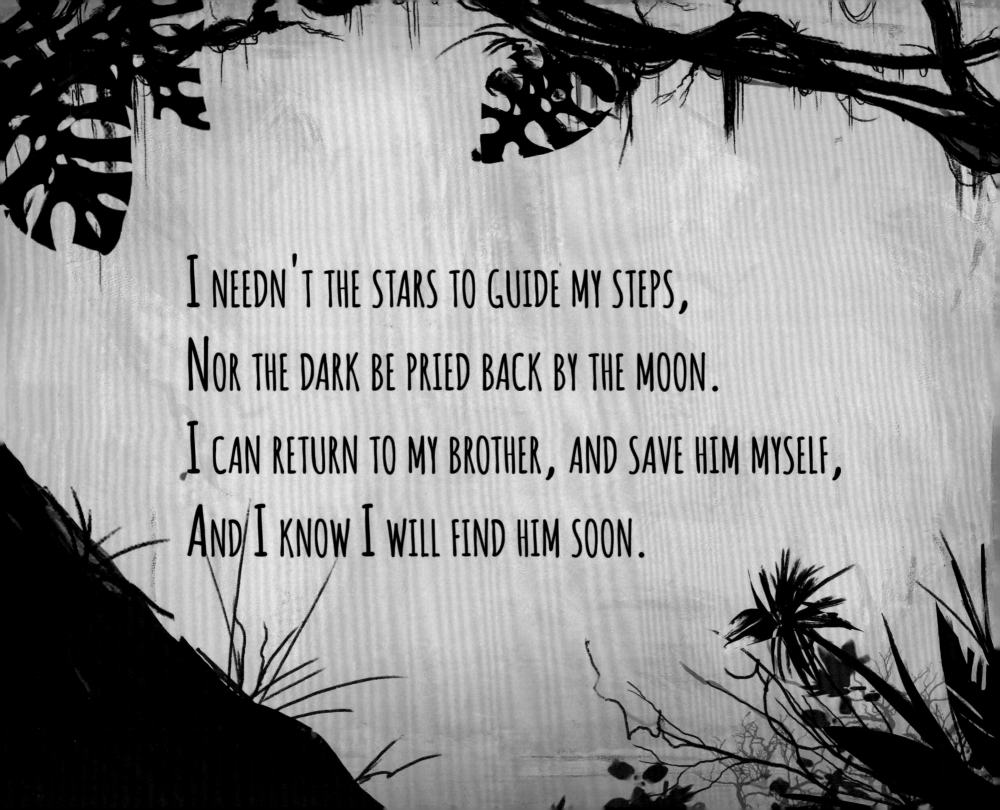

I needn't the stars to guide my steps,
Nor the dark be pried back by the moon.
I can return to my brother, and save him myself,
And I know I will find him soon.

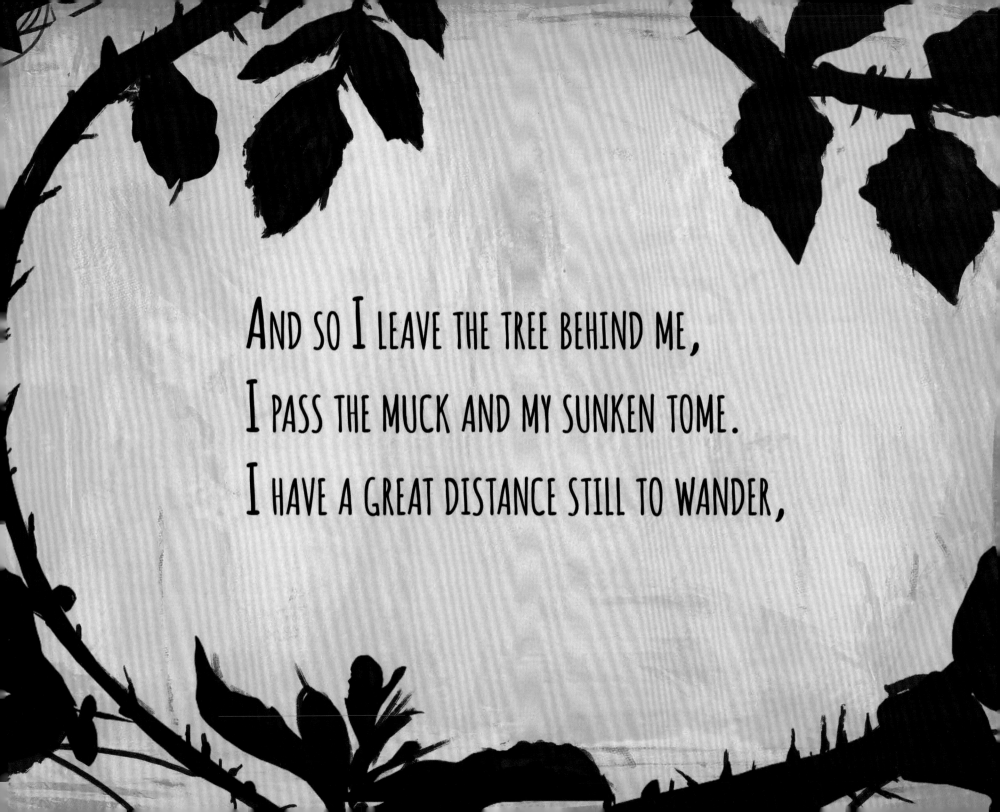

And so I leave the tree behind me,
I pass the muck and my sunken tome.
I have a great distance still to wander,

And a great many places yet to roam.

About the Author

MATT CUBBERLY works as an author and screenwriter. After founding The WilderWay LLC, he works to bring together the best aspects of both books and film – to write stories that entertain like a movie, and to write film scripts that can tell the great stories of a book. Having recently graduated from the University of Colorado at Boulder, he now lives in Arlington Heights, Illinois, focusing on the slightly weird – yet wonderfully wild.

About the Illustrator

IRINA KOVALOVA is a concept artist and illustrator originally from Latvia. Currently working in Glasgow, Scotland, Irina strives to tell stories through whimsical visuals, giving readers a beautiful look into a book's world before they even have a chance to read a word.